How Many Days Has Baby to Play?

joan walsh anglund

GULLIVER BOOKS · HARCOURT BRACE JOVANOVICH

San Diego   Austin   Orlando

Requests for permission to make copies of any part of the work should be mailed to:
Permissions, Harcourt Brace Jovanovich, Publishers, Orlando, Florida 32887.

Library of Congress Cataloging-in-Publication Data
Anglund, Joan Walsh.
How many days has Baby to play?
"Gulliver books."
Summary: Bear and Baby romp through the seven
days of the week.
[1. Days—Fiction. 2. Teddy Bears—Fiction.
3. Babies—Fiction. 4. Play—Fiction.
5. Stories in rhyme] I. Title.
PZ8.3.A549Hq 1988   [E]   87-19665
ISBN 0-15-200460-2

Printed and bound in Hong Kong
by South China Printing Company

First edition

A B C D E

for my dear friend

Helen Hyman

to share with

the children she loves

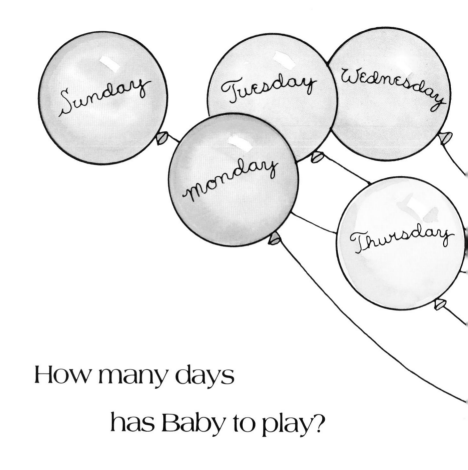

How many days

has Baby to play?

SUNDAY

we visit

and stroll down the way,

MONDAY

with our big, round ball

we play.

TUESDAY

we picnic

and swing

from a tree,

WEDNESDAY

it's toys for my bear and me.

THURSDAY

it's castles

and a kiddie-car ride,

FRIDAY

it's play school

and we go down

a slide.

SATURDAY

we seesaw,

just me

and my friend,

and that brings our
play days to a happy end.

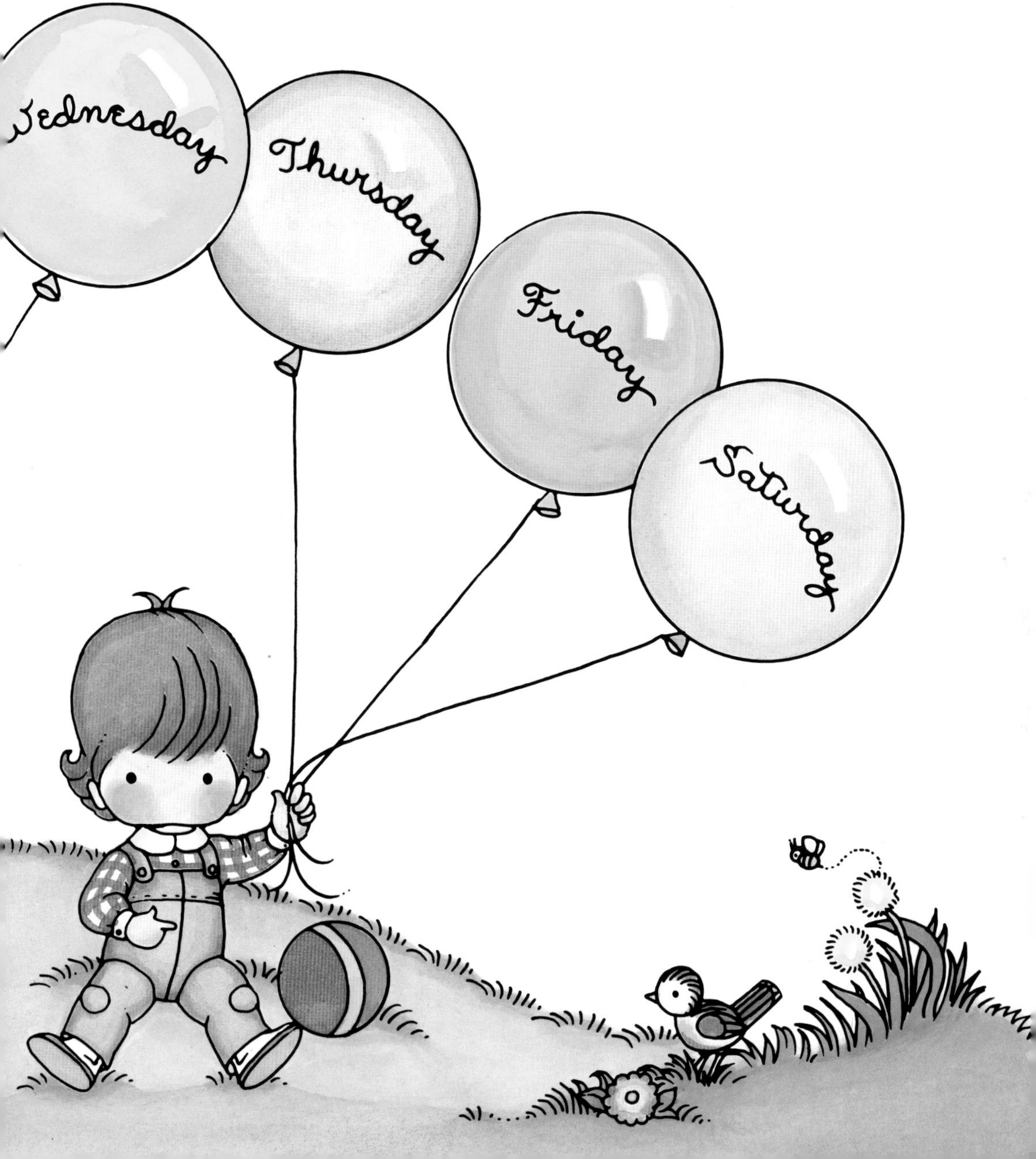
Wednesday
Thursday
Friday
Saturday

Seven days

    make one happy week

for Baby to play

    and to learn

      and to speak,

to hear and to touch,

    to run and to see,

and all of these days

    are for

Baby and me!

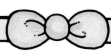

BY JOAN WALSH ANGLUND

A Friend Is Someone Who Likes You

The Brave Cowboy

Love Is a Special Way of Feeling

In a Pumpkin Shell

Christmas Is a Time of Giving

Nibble Nibble Mousekin

Spring Is a New Beginning

Childhood Is a Time of Innocence

Morning Is a Little Child

Do You Love Someone?

A Cup of Sun